JOYFUL COLOUR

Colour these beautiful illustrations
and soothe your mind

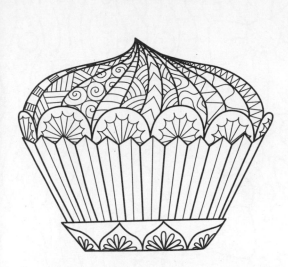

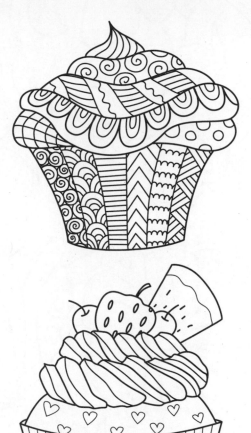

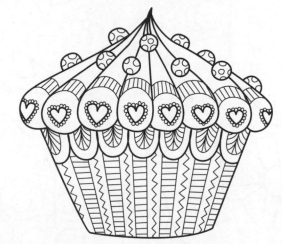

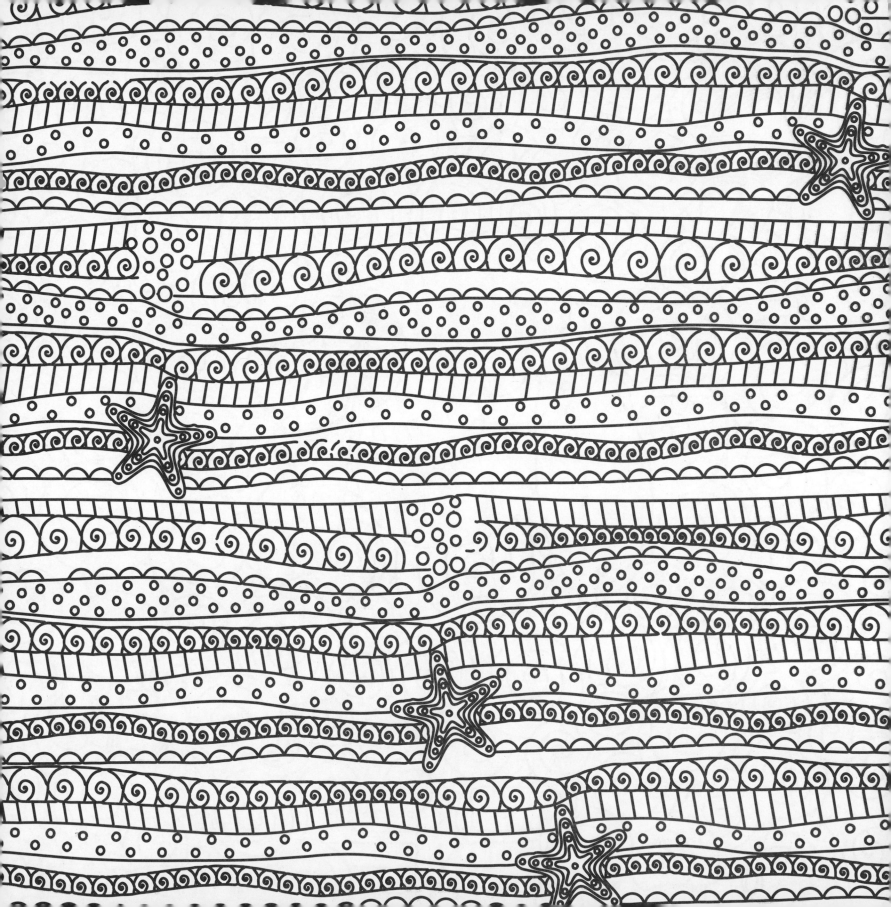

JOYFUL COLOUR

Colour these beautiful illustrations and soothe your mind

ADULT COLOURING BOOK
LIBRO PARA COLOREAR
PARA ADULTOS

TRY ME!
We'll refund or replace
if you are not happy
with our quality.

This does not affect your statutory rights

5 053834 381703 >

138170

© GE, PO Box 13657,
Birmingham B2 2FQ, UK